Dinosaur
COLORING BOOK

CREATIVE COLORING PRESS

Triceratops

Triceratops lived in the late Cretaceous period. They were up to 30 feet in length and weighed up to 5 tons. Their horns were used for defense.

Tyrannosaurus

Tyrannosaurus Rex means "Tyrant Lizard." The T. Rex was up to 40 feet in length and could run up to 20 miles per hour. They lived during the late Cretaceous period.

Stegosaurus

The Stegosaurus was one of the largest dinosaurs, up to 30 feet in length. It was a plant eater, or herbivore. The Stegosaurus used its powerful tail for defense. It lived during the late Jurassic period.

Nothronycus

Northronycus was a herbivore that lived in
North America during the Cretaceous period.
It had bird-like characteristics and may have
been covered in feathers. It was up to 20 feet
long and weighed about 2,200 pounds.

Ouranosaurus

Ouranosaurus was a slow-moving plant eater, or herbivore, about the size of an elephant. It lived in Africa during the early Cretaceous period, about 125 million years ago.

Garudimimus

The Garudimimus was an omnivore that lived during the late Cretaceous period. Its fossils have been found in Asia. It averaged 12 feet in length.

Parasaurolopus

Parasaurolopus were herbivores, or plant eaters. They used their crests for making trumpeting noises. They lived in the late Cretaceous period. They were up to 33 feet long and weighed about 3 tons.

Wuerhosaurus

The Wuerhosaurus was an herbivore that lived during the early Cretaceous period, about 130 million years ago. It lived in Asia. They were 27 feet long and weighed around 4 tons.

Brachiosaurus

Brachiosaurus were herbivores that lived in the late Jurassic period. They were up to 85 feet in length and weighed up to 40 tons. Scientists think they were warm-blooded animals, like mammals.

Ankylosaurus

The Ankylosaurus was an herbivore with large plates of body armor and a large clubbed tail for protection against pred-ators. It lived during the late Cretaceous period. They were large, 30 feet long and weighed more than 13,000 pounds.

Quaesitosaurus

Quaesitorsaurus was a long-necked and long-tailed herbivore. It was about 75 feet long. It lived during the late Cretaceous period. They were slow-moving dinosaurs.

Carnotaurus

Carnotaurus was a carnivore, or meat eater, that lived during the late Cretaceous period. It was about 25 feet in length and weighed around 2 tons. They lived in South America.

Juravenator

Juravenator was a small dinosaur, about 2 feet in length. It lived in Europe during the Jurassic period. They were partially feathered and ate insects and fish.

Diplodocus

Diplodocus lived toward the end of the Jurassic period. They were up to 88 feet long and weighed as much as a big truck, about 12 tons. They were herbivores with very small heads in proportion to the rest of their bodies.

Fukuisaurus

Fukuisaurus was an herbivore that lived
in Japan and Asia during the middle
Cretaceous period. They were about
15 feet long and weighed around 900
pounds.

Hypsilophodon

The Hypsilophodon was a small plant-eating dinosaur. It moved very fast on two legs. It was about 6.5 feet in length and weighed around 150 pounds. It lived in the early Cretaceous period.

Xenotarsosaurus

Xenotarsosaurus was a carnivore, or meat eater, that lived during the Cretaceous period. Its fossils have been found in South America. It was 18 feet in length and weighed up to 2000 pounds.

Kronosaurus

The Kronosaurus was a marine reptile and also a carnivore, or meat eater. They were up to 30 feet long. Kronosaurus was a plesiosaur, not a dinosaur. They lived during the early Cretaceous period.

Khaan

The Khaan was an omnivore that lived during the Cretaceous period, about 75 million years ago. Its fossils have been found in Mongolia in Central Asia. It was about 6 feet long.

Yinlong

Yinlong was an herbivore that lived in China during the Jurassic period. It was a small dinosaur, only 4 feet in length and weighed about 30 pounds.

Iguanodon

Iguanodons were herbivores, or plant eaters, that lived during the early Cretaceous period. They were up to 39 feet in length and weighed around 3 1/2 tons. Most Iguanodons lived in Europe.

Elaphrosaurus

Elasphrosaurus was meat-eating predator that lived during the Jurassic period, about 150 million years ago. It was 15 feet in length and weighed around 450 pounds.

Tylochepele

Tylochepele was a dome-headed dinosaur. It was an herbivore, or plant eater. It lived in Asia during the late Cretaceous period. It was about 6 feet long and weighed 110 pounds.

Mosasaurus

Mosasaurus were marine reptiles, not dinosaurs. They were related to today's monitor lizards. They were meat eaters, and although they lived in the water, they breathed air. They were up to 60 feet in length.

Velociraptor

Velociraptors were meat eaters, or carnivores, that lived about 75 million years ago during the Cretaceous period. They were smart, with large brains and are thought to have hunted in packs. They were 6 feet long and weighed about 55 pounds.

Urbacodon

The Urbacodon was a small carnivore, or meat-eating, dinosaur that lived during the late Cretaceous period. It was about 3 feet long and weighed around 20 pounds.

Pterodactyl

Pterodactyls were flying reptiles that lived during the late Jurassic period. They had a 3-foot wingspan and reproduced by laying eggs. They had lightweight wings and could fly long distances.

Zephyrosaurus

The Zephyrosaurus was a small plant-eating dinosaur that lived in North America during the Cretaceous period. They were 6 feet long and weighed around 80 pounds.

Liaoxiornis

Liaoxiornis was a prehistoric feathered bird that lived during the Cretaceous period in China. It had a short skull and teeth.

Rebbachisaurus

The Rebbachisaurus was an herbivore, or plant-eating dinosaur, that lived during the early Cretaceous period. It lived in Northern Africa in Morocco. It was up to 65 feet long and weighed around 7 tons.

Dinosaur Facts

- Dinosaurs lived in the **Mesozioc Era**, 250 to 65 million years ago.

- The Mesozioc Era was divided into three parts:
  - **Triassic period** (250-200 million years ago)
  - **Jurassic period** (200-145 million years ago)
  - **Cretaceous period** (145-65 million years ago)

- During the Mesozioc Era there was a single large continent called **Pangaea**. This continent eventually separated into the continents we have today.

- Many scientists believe the dinosaurs went extinct due to a large asteroid or comet hitting the Earth.

70639690R00038

Made in the USA
Middletown, DE
15 April 2018